Advice for parents

This book is designed for children to complet
but you may like to work with them for the firs. .ew pages.
They can work through the book unit by unit, or can dip in
and out to practise a particular skill. The *Practice Workbook*
range is easy to use as stand-alone workbooks. They also
complement the Practice series, which is full of explanations
and examples.

From May 2013 there is a new compulsory test in English
Grammar, Spelling and Punctuation for children aged 11.
Previously the English test was divided into Reading and
Writing, and so grammar was only assessed as part of
written composition, and spelling by a dictation test.

The new test puts an emphasis on knowing the terminology
of grammar: word classes, phrases and clauses, prefixes
and suffixes. There is also an extension up to a Level 6 test,
and this book covers enough content to prepare children
fully for Level 6.

This book is therefore designed both to help children
prepare for the new test, and to equip them with skills for
later life in effective and accurate communication.

The new Key Stage 2 test

This *Practice Workbook* will help you feel prepared for the new English Grammar, Punctuation and Spelling test.

We have arranged ours in the order **Spelling, Grammar, Punctuation** because spelling is about getting your letters right, grammar is about getting your words right, and punctuation is about getting your sentences right, so this seemed a good order for learning.

Here are a few sample questions to show you what the layout of the test will be like.

1 Draw lines to match each sentence with the most likely final punctuation.

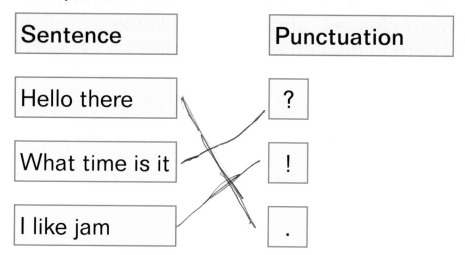

Sentence	Punctuation
Hello there	?
What time is it	!
I like jam	.

2a Circle the apostrophe in this sentence:

"If it's raining tomorrow, we could swim instead."

2b Why is the apostrophe needed? Tick one answer.

to indicate possession ☒

to indicate a change of subject ☑

to mark a missing letter ☒

because it's a main clause ☑

3a Which word could fill the gap in this sentence? Tick one box.

He invited my friend and ___.

there's ☐

I ☐

he ☐

me ☑

3b Tick the term that describes the word you have chosen:

relative pronoun ☐

object pronoun ☐

contraction ☐

adverb ☑

By the end of this book, you should feel confident about answering all these questions!

1: Spelling – Prefixes

Spelling gets easier if you break words down into their separate parts.

This is what the parts are called:

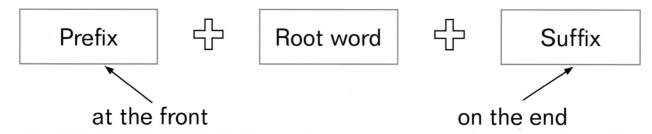

| Prefix | | Root word | | Suffix |

at the front   on the end

For example: dis-trust-ing, re-boot-ed, un-help-ful

Activity 1

Join each prefix to one of these root words, then write the meaning of the new word.

market	marine	city	take	fab
biotic	appear	do	graph	place
correct				

Prefix	Meaning	New word	Meaning
un-	not		
in-	not		
dis-	not		
mis-	not		
pre-	before		
re-	again		
sub-	under		
inter-	between		
super-	above		
anti-	against		
auto-	self		

Activity 2

Write sentences using each of your new words from page 6.

1 _____

2 _____

3 _____

4 _____

5 _____

6 _____

7 _____

8 _____

9 _____

10 _____

11 _____

Activity 3

Some prefixes come from Greek and Latin. Fill in words with these prefixes.

Prefix	Meaning	Sample words
bi-	two	
tri-	three	
micro-	small	
tele-	distant	
trans-	across	
circum-	around	
aqua-	water	
ped-	foot	

2: Spelling – Suffixes

Now let's look at the end part of the word:

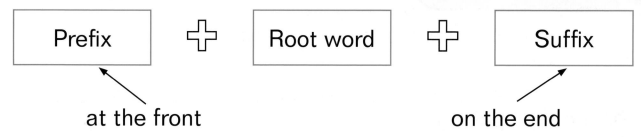

| Prefix | ➕ | Root word | ➕ | Suffix |

at the front   on the end

The suffix could be **-ed**, **-er**, **-ing**, **-ful**, **-tion** and many more.

Activity 1

Here are two suffixes to add to adjectives.

The first, **-ness**, turns them into nouns. The second, **-ly**, turns them into adverbs.

Remember the rule for endings in **-y**: change to **i**, before adding the suffix.

	-ness	-ly
happy		
airy		
bold		
tidy		
easy		
cool		
cosy		
daft		
holy		
fair		
lazy		
woolly		
busy		

Activity 2

Now you think of words with these vowel sounds, but choose ones that all begin with **d**.

	Short vowel sound	Long vowel sound
a		
e		
i		
o		
u		

Activity 3

Write pairs of words with **magic e** spelling.

1 mat   _____

2 met   _____

3 bit   _____

4 rod   _____

5 dun   _____

6 _____ shame

7 _____ Pete

8 _____ fine

9 _____ hope

10 _____ tune

4: Spelling – Suffixes after short vowels

Now let's take verbs with short vowel sounds and add endings beginning with vowels: **-ing**, **-ed** and **-er**.

Activity 1

If they end with two or three consonants, it's easy: you just add the ending.

Fill in these words.

	-ing	-ed	-er
flick			
tend			
sift			
sand			
bump			
long			
clang			
hang			
knock			
wreck			

Activity 2

If the word ends with **-x**, it also counts as a **two-consonant** sound.

	-ing	-ed	-er
mix			
fix			
box			

Activity 3

But if the root word has a short vowel sound and ends with a single consonant, you have to double that consonant before you add the ending. Fill in all these words.

	-ing	-ed	-er
slim	slimming	slimmed	slimmer
trap			
stop			
mat			
bet			
pat			
dip			
wet			
pot			
fit			
rot			
ham			
shop			
sup			

Activity 4

Now you can test the rule.
For each word below, give the right spelling for a long vowel sound.

Short vowels	Long vowels	Short vowels	Long vowels
twinning		mopping	
canned		matted	
stripped		pipped	
tinny		fussing	
robbed		pinning	
bonny		supper	
tapping		dinner	

5: Spelling – Suffix -ant and -ent

There are several adjectives spelt with a suffix of -**ant** or -**ent**.

They are often linked to the spelling of the related verb and noun.

Activity 1

Fill in the -**ant** adjectives.

Verb	Noun	Adjective
hesitate	hesitation	hesitant
dominate	domination	
jubilate	jubilation	
stagnate	stagnation	
expect	expectation	
observe	observation	
tolerate	tolerance	
ignore	ignorance	
abound	abundance	
resound	resonance	

Activity 2

Some nouns also end with -**ant**.

Verbs	Noun	Verbs	Noun
depend	dependant	immigrate	
attend		litigate	
assist		occupy	
claim			

With -**ent** adjectives, their spelling is again linked to the related noun.

Nouns	Adjective
innocence	innocent
lenience	
obedience	
affluence	
confidence	
decadence	
impudence	
independence	
coherence	
indulgence	
diligence	
convergence	
divergence	
emergence	
decency	
frequency	
eloquence	

6: Spelling – Suffix -able and -ible

Activity 1

Most adjectives with this sound are spelt -able, and have related verbs and nouns.

Verb	Noun	Adjective
adore	adoration	adorable
apply	application	
consider	consideration	
observe	observation	
tolerate	tolerance	
understand	understanding	
reason	reasoning	
comfort	comforting	
enjoy	enjoying	
fix	fixing	

Activity 2

As the suffix -able starts with a vowel, you have to check the spelling.

- After a short vowel sound with single consonant, double the last consonant.
- Change y to i if it comes after a consonant.
- You can drop the final e, except after **soft consonants** like **g** and **c**.

Root word	Adjective	Root word	Adjective
stop	stoppable	move	
bid		change	
rely		notice	
size		service	
like		belief	

Activity 3

Adjectives ending in **-ible** usually don't have obvious root words.

Write these **-ible** adjectives from the clues.

1 Can be done: p_____

2 Horrid: h_____

3 Can be read: l_____

4 Can't be credited: inc_____

5 Full of sense: s_____

6 Giving terror: t_____

7 Can be seen: v_____

Activity 4

Now, to practise them all again, copy these adjectives into the right jars.

lovable	credible	horrible	possible
reliable	unflappable	visible	changeable
feasible	winnable		

-able

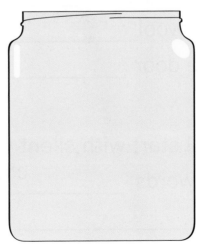

-ible

7: Spelling – Silent letters

Some tricky words have letters that we don't sound at all, like lam**b** or **k**night or this**t**le.

Let's make groups of these words.

Silent b

These words all end with silent **b**.

1 Next to your fingers _____

2 A small sheep _____

3 A tiny bit of bread _____

Silent g

These words all start with silent **g**.

4 A garden figure _____

5 To chew _____

6 To grind your teeth _____

Silent k

These words all start with silent **k**.

7 Use for cutting _____

8 Make with wool _____

9 Rap on the door _____

Silent w

These words all start with silent **w**.

10 Put down words _____

11 Not right _____

12 Between hand and arm _____

Activity 2

Ask someone to give you this dictation.

They read each line aloud, pausing at each underlined word for you to write it down.

Each of those words has a silent letter!

1 I hurt my <u>knee</u> and then I hurt my <u>wrist</u>.

2 His hands were <u>gnarled</u>, and he had deep <u>wrinkles</u>.

3 When I read your <u>writing</u>, it tells me what I need to <u>know</u>.

4 The medieval <u>knight</u> rode away from the <u>shipwreck</u>.

5 A little fluffy <u>wren</u> is perched on the garden <u>gnome</u>.

6 Polish the door <u>knocker</u>; then do your <u>knitting</u>.

7 I picked up the <u>knife</u>, which must be <u>wrong</u>.

Activity 3

Now we can return to the **-gh** spellings, which of course are silent letters.

1 Opposite of day _____

2 Opposite of dark _____

3 Opposite of loose _____

4 Opposite of wrong _____

5 Opposite of dull _____

6 Past tense of buy _____

7 Past tense of fight _____

8 Past tense of seek _____

9 Past tense of think _____

10 Past tense of catch _____

11 Past tense of teach _____

8: Spelling – Homophones

Words that sound the same but have different meanings are often spelt differently.

These words are called homophones.

Activity 1

First, let's practise those words that have **c** for a noun and **s** for a verb.

Fill in the gaps.

Noun	Verb
practice	
licence	
prophecy	
	devise
	advise

Activity 2

Next, try writing sample sentences for each of these (check page 24 for word classes).

1 Passed as a verb _____

2 Past as a noun _____

3 Past as an adjective _____

4 Past as a preposition _____

5 Past as an adverb _____

Activity 3

Now write definitions of each pair of homophones.

Check in your dictionary if you're not sure of their meanings.

1. boarder/border _A boarder comes to stay; a border lies between two countries._

2. billed/build _____

3. bold/bowled _____

4. break/brake _____

5. ceiling/sealing _____

6. draft/draught _____

7. find/fined _____

8. guilt/gilt _____

9. heart/hart _____

10. horde/hoard _____

11. knead/need _____

12. lava/larva _____

13. law/lore _____

14. miner/minor _____

15. muscle/mussel _____

16. medal/meddle _____

17. pedal/peddle _____

18. place/plaice _____

19. profit/prophet _____

20. root/route _____

21. rough/ruff _____

22. sauce/source _____

9: Spelling – Words to learn

In the National Tests (SATs) at age 11, the Spelling test is a dictation given to you by your teacher.

That test gives the words in context, which means that the dictation is a passage that includes 20 words you have to write down.

But why not ask someone to give you a dictation of these words on their own, so that you can see how many you get right? Or you could say the letters when someone reads the words to you.

Then you could grade the words, by those you got first time, and those you had to go back to again.

accommodate	embarrass
achieve	environment
ancient	equipped
appreciate	exaggerate
attached	excellent
available	explanation
awkward	foreign
bruise	forty
category	frequently
cemetery	government
committee	guarantee
competition	harass
conscious	hindrance
correspond	identity
curiosity	immediately
definite	interfere
develop	interrupt

language

leisure

lightning

marvellous

mischievous

muscle

necessary

nuisance

occur

opportunity

parliament

persuade

physical

prejudice

privilege

profession

pronunciation

queue

recommend

relevant

restaurant

rhyme

rhythm

sacrifice

secretary

shoulder

signature

stomach

suggest

symbol

system

temperature

thorough

twelfth

variety

vegetable

vehicle

yacht

Word classes are sometimes called parts of speech.

They tell you what job a word does in a sentence. The main word classes are:

- **nouns**, which are naming words, like **cat**, **sadness**, **Paris**
- **verbs**, which are doing words, like **skip**, **skipping**, **skipped**
- **adjectives**, which are describing words, like **red**, **quick**, **my**
- **adverbs**, which tell **how**, **when** or **where** a verb happens, like **quickly**, **yesterday**, **there**
- **pronouns**, which stand instead of nouns, like **I**, **me**, **mine**
- **prepositions**, which come before (*pre*) a noun to describe its **position**, like **near**, **at**, **beside**.

If you know what job a word is doing in a sentence, it will help improve your writing.

To change a word into a different word class, you often change the ending.

Noun	Adjective	Verb
horror	horrid	horrify

Activity 1

You may know these words already, or you may need to check them in your dictionary.

They all follow different patterns!

Noun	Adjective	Verb
terror	terrible	terrify
harmony		
glory		
peace		
belief		
practice		
advice		
glamour		
success		
fat		

A dictionary is the most useful way of improving your spelling and your grammar.

Whether it's online or in print, these are the things you can look up:

- How to spell a word
- What word class it is
- Other forms of the root word
- What it means
- How it's used in a sample sentence

Activity 1

Look at the page opposite, and answer these questions.

1 Which are the only two adjectives on the page?

_____

2 If you weren't sure how to spell the word 'public', how would you start to look?

_____

3 What other form of noun is given after the headword?

_____

4 What suffixes are given for verbs?

_____

5 Which word has more than one meaning?

_____

6 What typeface is used for sample sentences?

_____

7 Which of these words did you not know already?

_____

a
b
c
d
e
f
g
h
i
j
k
l
m
n
o
p
q
r
s
t
u
v
w
x
y
z

prove *verb* (**proves, proving, proved**)
To prove that something is true means to show that it is definitely true. ▸ *These footprints prove that someone has been in the garden.*

proverb *noun* (*plural* **proverbs**)
a short, well-known saying which gives you advice about something

provide *verb* (**provides, providing, provided**)
If you provide something for people, you give it to them. ▸ *The school provides us with books and pencils.*

prowl *verb* (**prowls, prowling, prowled**)
To prowl means to walk around very quietly and secretly.

prune *noun* (*plural* **prunes**)
a dried plum

pry *verb* (**pries, prying, pried**)
If you pry, you try to find out about something that has nothing to do with you. ▸ *You shouldn't pry into other people's business.*

pub *noun* (*plural* **pubs**)
a place where people can go to have a drink and meet friends

public *adjective*
Something that is public can be used by everyone. ▸ *Is there a public swimming pool in your town?*

publish *verb* (**publishes, publishing, published**)
To publish a book means to print it and sell it.

pudding *noun* (*plural* **puddings**)
any sweet food which you eat after the main part of a meal ▸ *What are we having for pudding?*

puddle *noun* (*plural* **puddles**)
a small pool of water

puff *verb* (**puffs, puffing, puffed**)
1 When a train puffs, it blows out smoke as it goes along.
2 If you are puffing, you are out of breath because you have been running.

puffin *noun* (*plural* **puffins**)
a bird that lives near the sea and has a large orange and blue beak

pull *verb* (**pulls, pulling, pulled**)
When you pull something, you get hold of it and move it towards you.

pullover *noun* (*plural* **pullovers**)
a jumper

pulse *noun*
Your pulse is the regular pumping of blood round your body. You can feel your pulse in your neck or wrist.

pump *noun* (*plural* **pumps**)
a machine that pushes air or water into something or out of something ▸ *You use a bicycle pump to put air into tyres.*

pump *verb* (**pumps, pumping, pumped**)
When you pump water or air, you force it into something or out of something.
▸ *The firemen pumped all the water out of the flooded house.*

pumpkin *noun* (*plural* **pumpkins**)
a very large, round orange vegetable

pun *noun* (*plural* **puns**)
a joke that is funny because it uses words that sound the same, or words that have two different meanings. For example, 'eggs are very eggs- pensive' is a pun.

punch *verb* (**punches, punching, punched**)
If you punch someone, you hit them with your fist.

punctual *adjective*
If you are punctual, you arrive exactly on time.

punctuation *noun*
all the marks such as commas and full stops that you put into a piece of writing to make it easier to read

puncture *noun* (*plural* **punctures**)
a small hole in a tyre

We have lots of different ways of communicating with each other.

- Speaking to each other.
- Texting or messaging each other.
- Writing informal emails or notes.
- Writing reports and formal documents.

These are called different **modes** of language, and there are different styles or **conventions** for each.

For each of these modes, suggest vocabulary or types of words that are appropriate to use.

1 Speaking to each other

_____

_____

2 Texting or messaging each other

_____

_____

3 Writing informal emails or notes

_____

_____

4 Writing formal documents

_____

_____

Convert each of these informal spoken or texting lines into formal or written grammar, or what is called 'Standard English'. Then write more parallel examples of your own.

1 Like, I never seed him before.

_____

2 It's like I never been gone.

_____

3 You done well.

_____

4 I'm doing good.

_____

5 u shall luv ur mobile fone with all ur hart

_____

6 The Gr8 Db8

_____

7 2b or not 2b

_____

8 _____

_____

9 _____

_____

10 _____

_____

13: Grammar – Noun phrases

The mark schemes for the National Tests give a lot of credit for use of expanded noun phrases.

Here are examples of how a noun can be expanded into longer noun phrases.

- jersey
- the yellow jersey
- the yellow jersey worn by Bradley Wiggins
- the yellow jersey worn by Bradley Wiggins in the Tour de France

These are all phrases, as there is no verb included.

Activity 1

Expand each of these nouns into longer noun phrases in a similar way:

1 jacket

_____

_____

_____

2 wheel

_____

_____

_____

3 house

_____

_____

_____

4 town

_____

_____

_____

When a noun or noun phrase is used in a sentence, it may be the **subject** or the **object** of a verb.

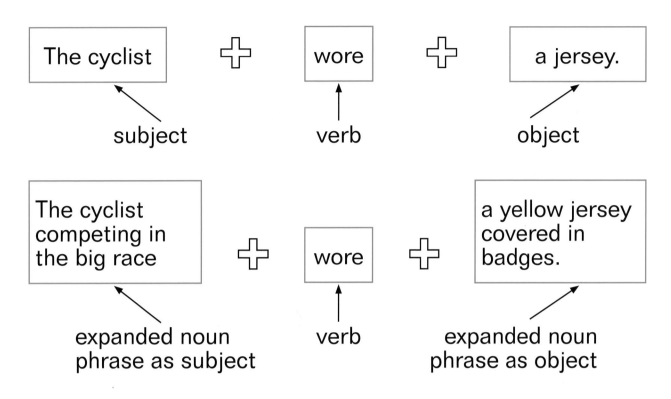

Write expanded subject or object noun phrases to complete these sentences.

1 The cyclist pushed _____

2 The swimmer wore _____

3 The runner forgot _____

4 _____ lost the final part of the race.

5 _____ missed the closing ceremony.

6 _____ became a great hero.

Now we've practised nouns as subjects and objects, it's a good time to practise pronouns again.

With pronouns, the example on page 31 becomes:

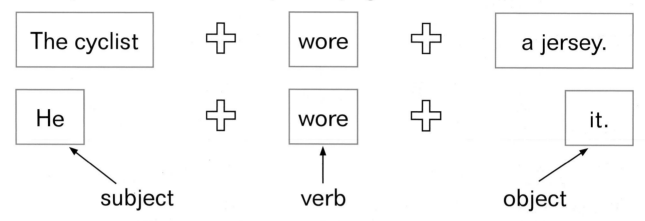

| The cyclist | ✚ | wore | ✚ | a jersey. |

| He | ✚ | wore | ✚ | it. |

subject   verb   object

Here is a reminder of the subject and object pronouns.

	Subject	Object
1st person	I, we	me, us
2nd person	you	you
3rd person	he, she, it, they, who	him, her, it, them, whom

Activity 1

Replace each noun with a pronoun.

1 The boy lost his bicycle.

_____

2 His mother was cross with the boy.

_____

3 The boy accused his friends.

_____

4 The friends came to see the boy and me.

_____

5 The mother found the bicycle before the boy did.

_____

6 The mother and boy were both pleased.

_____

Let's now learn possessive pronouns: that's **mine**, not **yours**, nor **hers**.

Possessive pronouns **never** have apostrophes.

	Singular	Plural
1st person	mine	ours
2nd person	yours	yours
3rd person	his, hers, its	theirs

Replace the words in brackets with possessive pronouns.

1 My bike goes faster than (my brother's) _____.

2 My bike is smaller than (my sister's) _____.

3 Your car is bigger than (your parents') _____.

4 (My scooter) _____ is faster than (my brother's) _____.

5 (Our grandparents' car) _____ is bigger than (our family's) _____.

15: Grammar – Verbs

Verbs can be active or passive, if they have a subject and an object.

An active verb looks like this: I <u>sent</u> the letter.

A passive verb looks like this: The letter <u>was sent</u> by me.

With an active verb, the subject usually comes first ('I' in the example).

With a passive verb, the object usually comes first ('the letter' in the example).

Active verbs make the narrative more active and dramatic.

Passive verbs make the narrative more formal, as in scientific writing.

◯ Activity 1

Rewrite these sentences in the passive. Notice which other words it is better to change.

1 Everyone watched the news today.

_____

2 The figures struck us as horrifying.

_____

3 The newsreader told us what would happen next.

_____

4 All of us thought it was a disaster.

_____

5 Nobody remembered anything similar.

_____

6 Everyone will remember it for a long time.

_____

Activity 2

Now change these sentences from passive to active.

Again, notice which words you change, apart from the verb.

1 Experiments are fully researched by scientists.

_____

2 Their notes are usually written with long sentences.

_____

3 Their research is published in journals.

_____

4 The journals are read by very few people.

_____

5 Lots of prizes are awarded to scientists.

_____

6 Will they be remembered by anyone?

_____

Activity 3

Another kind of verb we must include is the imperative, which we use for command sentences. For example:

- Shut the door.
- Open the window.
- Come inside.

Choose an imperative verb to write at the beginning of each of these command sentences.

1 _____ the table.

2 _____ your hair.

3 _____ the tickets.

4 _____ your shoes.

16: Grammar – Adverbs

Adverbs tell us more about a verb: they say **how**, **when** or **where** the verb happens.

Adverbs have comparative and superlative versions, just as adjectives do.

Adverb	Comparative	Superlative
quickly	more quickly	most quickly
safely	more safely	most safely

There are just a few adverbs that can be made comparative in one word.

Adverb	Comparative	Superlative
fast	faster	fastest
early	earlier	earliest
hard	harder	hardest
well	better	best
badly	worse	worst
far	farther	farthest

Activity 1

Write comparative and superlative adverbs here.

1. My scooter goes quietly, his goes _____, hers goes _____.

2. I work hard, she works _____, he works _____.

3. She runs swiftly, I run _____, he runs _____.

4. My test went badly, his went _____, hers went _____.

5. He ran far, she ran _____, I ran _____.

6. I arrived early, he arrived _____, she arrived _____.

Adverbs can be built into longer phrases, just as with noun phrases.

How	When	Where
Quietly	Tomorrow	Near
Quietly with his shoes in his hand,	Tomorrow before midday,	Near the old oak tree,

Activity 2

Write adverbial phrases at the beginning, at the end, or in the middle of these sentences.

Remember that phrases don't include verbs.

1. **(How)** _____, she came in the room.

2. **(When)** _____, she came in the room.

3. **(Where)** _____, she came in the room.

4. He left the room, **(how)** _____.

5. He left the room, **(when)** _____.

6. He left the room, **(where)** _____.

7. They surprised us, **(how)** _____, and so we left.

8. They surprised us, **(when)** _____, and so we left.

9. They surprised us, **(where)** _____, and so we left.

17: Grammar – Prepositions

Prepositions precede nouns.

They can be grouped into prepositions of **place**, **time** and **cause**.

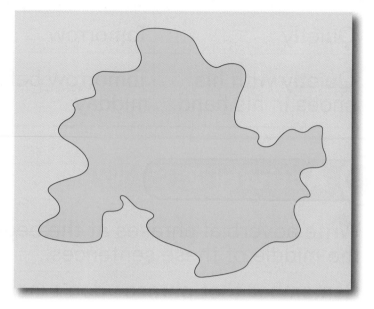

Activity 1

Let's revise **prepositions of place** first.

Draw a map of a dream holiday island, and mark all the things to do.

Write **five** sentences about *where* you'd like to go, using prepositions, for example: **along** the beach.

1 _____

2 _____

3 _____

4 _____

5 _____

Here are some prepositions of place to choose from:

above	across	against	along	among
around	behind	below	beneath	beside
between	beyond	down	in	inside
into	near	on	onto	out
outside	over	past	through	toward
under	underneath	upon	within	

Activity 2

Now let's turn to **prepositions of time**.

These include: **after, before, during, from, in, since, till, until**.

Write five sentences about **when** you'd like to travel.

Remember, each preposition should be followed by a noun.

1 _____

2 _____

3 _____

4 _____

5 _____

Activity 3

Finally, let's look at **prepositions of cause**.

Examples are: **for, from, through, because of, on account of**.

Write **five** sentences about **why** you'd like to escape.

Again, each preposition should be followed by a noun.

1 _____

2 _____

3 _____

4 _____

5 _____

18: Grammar – Relative clauses

So far we've looked at noun **phrases** and adverbial **phrases**, neither of which included verbs.

Now we shall start to look at **clauses** within sentences, and **clauses** always include a **verb**.

One of the most common is the **relative clause**, introduced by **who**, **whom**, **where**, **when**, **which** and **whose** (which are called **relative pronouns**):

● Jack and Jill, **who are well known to us all**, were going to the moon.

Activity 1

Underline the verbs in these relative clauses.

1 The spaceship, which was designed by Jill, was ready for take-off.

2 Jill was taking Jack, who was her favourite companion.

3 They were going to the moon, where they would land that afternoon.

4 It was breakfast time when the alarm went off.

5 Jack, with whom Jill shared a suitcase, packed their things.

6 Jill followed Jack, whose suitcase was already loaded, onto the spaceship.

Activity 2

Add relative clauses to these sentences, making sure each has a verb, as it's a clause.

1 The spaceship was all ready, when _____.

2 Their target was the moon, where _____.

3 The captain was Jill, who _____.

4 Her companion was Jack, whom _____.

5 The spaceship, which _____, then took off.

6 The route, whose _____, took them past several planets.

Activity 3

A relative clause may be the object of a main verb.

- He told us **when we were going**.
- She showed us **where we'd be staying**.
- I asked **whom they preferred**.

Write relative clauses to follow these main verbs.

1 He stayed where _____.

2 She arrived when _____.

3 She asked why _____.

4 I suggested who _____.

5 They said which _____.

6 We asked whose _____.

7 He told us whom _____.

Now copy out the verbs from your relative clauses above.

1 _____

2 _____

3 _____

4 _____

5 _____

6 _____

7 _____

19: Grammar – Conjunctions

To combine separate clauses into more complex sentences, you can use either **relative pronouns** or **conjunctions**.

Activity 1

Join these pairs of sentences with a relative pronoun (**who, whom, where, when, which, whose**).

1 Those are my socks. Their holes need darning.

_____

2 I buy my socks at that shop. There's a cafe upstairs.

_____

3 I bought them last week. I really needed them.

_____

4 I shall give them to my sister. She likes them too.

_____

Activity 2

You can also join sentences with different **conjunction** words, like **and, as, but, or, nor, for, yet, so, although, because, since** and **unless**. Choose a conjunction to join each of these pairs of sentences.

1 I'm on the bus. I'm going swimming.

_____

2 It's cold outside. It's warm in the pool.

_____

3 I'll meet my friends there. They all go there too.

_____

4 We like the other pool better. It's longer.

_____

These conjunctions can be split into conjunctions of **time** or **cause**.

Time		Cause	
first	before	because	although
then	next	however	if
after	when	whereas	since

Activity 3

Join these sentences with different conjunctions of **time**.

1 I get up. I have my breakfast.

_____

2 I eat lunch. I go out to play.

_____

3 I have tea. I meet my friends.

_____

4 I play games. I go to bed.

_____

Activity 4

Join these sentences with different conjunctions of **cause**.

1 I'm hungry. I eat my tea.

_____

2 I'm thirsty. I get a drink.

_____

3 I'm tired. I go to sleep.

_____

4 I'm tired. I can't sleep.

_____

We have studied the grammar of phrases, which you'll remember never have verbs.

Now let's practise punctuating phrases, to separate them from the main clause.

Activity 1

Put commas round these phrases, where they are needed.

1 Coming in softly he made no noise at all.

2 For the last time don't forget the butter!

3 I always think staying in the country that it's the best place to be.

4 My home round the corner from the canal is easy to find.

5 I always daydream on the way home.

6 That's where you'll find me just north of the canal.

Activity 2

Commas are definitely needed if the phrase comes before or in the middle of the main clause.

But when the phrase comes after the main clause, it depends more on the sense.

1 I'm always hungry coming home from school.

2 I really enjoy my tea after a hard day's football practice.

3 I'm going out this evening always a nice thing to do.

4 I'll be back early probably very tired.

5 Then it's school tomorrow my favourite lessons of the week.

If the phrase is necessary to the sense of the main verb, as in 1 and 2, you would not separate it with a comma.

If a phrase is the subject of a sentence, the subject should never be separated from its verb.

People make this common error because they want to put commas where they pause in reading.

Activity 3

These sentences all have errors of punctuation. Rewrite them correctly.

1 Getting up late and missing breakfast, is never a good idea.

_____

2 The man with the hairy beard and messy hair, was waiting at the bus stop.

_____

3 The girl with the dragon tattoo, is a scary person.

_____

4 The girl, her sister and her dolls, are all packed and ready.

_____

5 Despite the rain, wearing wellington boots, still looks silly.

_____

Activity 4

Now write your own sentences with phrases before, in the middle and after the main clause.

Think carefully about where you put the commas.

_____

_____

_____

21: Grammar and Punctuation – Clauses

Let's look at relative clauses again (see pages 40 and 41), this time concentrating on the punctuation.

Activity 1

Add a relative clause to the end of each of these sentences, using the relative pronoun given.

Make sure you always separate the clause with a comma.

1 The spaceship landed on the moon. **(where)**

_____

2 It was due last week. **(when)**

_____

3 It was a strange spaceship. **(which)**

_____

Activity 2

Now add a relative clause in the middle of each of these sentences.

Check you've used two commas each time.

1 The alien **(who...)** was left behind.

_____

2 His friend **(whose...)** was sad to say goodbye.

_____

3 The one on the left **(whom...)** was even sadder.

_____

4 The launch pad **(where...)** was made of cheese.

_____

5 It left at 6 o'clock **(when...)** just in time for tea.

_____

There are some particular relative clauses **that** don't have commas, and use 'that' instead of 'which'.

These are called **defining clauses**.

- The cat **that ate the cream** is the one I like the best.
- The cat, **which was eating the cream**, is one I like a lot.

Can you tell the difference in meaning?

The first sentence defines which one of many cats I like the best.

The second sentence just describes one cat, with more information.

Activity 3

Add punctuation to those relative clauses that need commas.

1 I'll add commas to those that need them.

2 The second sentence which definitely needs a comma is easier to do.

3 This is the second sentence that might need a comma.

4 This is a good exercise where commas are concerned.

5 The exercises that use commas are the best ones.

6 Those sentences that use commas are easier to do.

7 The last sentence which is missing a comma doesn't make sense.

8 This is the last sentence that I'm going to do.

22: Punctuation – Semicolons and colons

There are two very useful punctuation marks that help you break your sentences in different ways: the semicolon; and the colon.

The semicolon, or half colon, balances equal parts of a sentence:

- Half of him wanted to go; half of him wanted to stay.
- In the morning it rains; in the afternoon it rains harder.

Activity 1

Write second halves for these sentences.

1. Mornings are dreary; afternoons _____ .

2. At school I work hard; at home _____ .

3. Girls are imaginative and creative; boys _____ _____ .

4. Soldiers operate on land; sailors _____ .

Activity 2

There is usually a verb both sides of the semicolon.

Rewrite these sentences with semicolons and a verb following the semicolon.

1. At breakfast I like my milk cold, and at supper hot.
   At breakfast I like my milk cold; at supper I like it hot.

2. At lunch I drink cold water, and at supper juice.

   _____

3. In the summer it rains a lot, in the winter less so.

   _____

4. At bedtime I clean my teeth for two minutes, in the morning rather longer.

   _____

The colon is different: it sends the sense forward into the second part of the sentence.

It can also be used before a list, and so there doesn't have to be a verb following a colon.

Activity 3

Write second halves for these sentences.

1. I'm shopping this afternoon: for_____.
2. He looked strange: _____.
3. These are my beliefs:_____.
4. I've come up with a grand plan: _____.
5. I'll tell you when I come home:_____.

Activity 4

Now you write your own sentences with semicolons and colons.

Remember that the semicolon balances equal halves; the colon sends the sense forward.

_____

_____

_____

_____

_____

23: Punctuation – Dashes and brackets

The dash is used rather often – instead of more formal punctuation.

But don't use it too often: colons and semicolons are good instead.

Activity 1

Rewrite these sentences *without* dashes.

1 I expect he'll be late – he usually is.

_____

2 What's the world coming to – I wish I knew.

_____

3 He said it was for charity – that's his story, anyway.

_____

4 I know I said it – and I meant it.

_____

Activity 2

A pair of dashes can be used to close off part of a sentence, in the same way as brackets.

We call this 'in parenthesis'; and there must always be a dash both sides of the parenthesis.

Add the missing dashes to these sentences.

1 The newer house – built this century is in the grounds of the old house.

2 The drive – leading up to the old house is moss and gravel.

3 The roof – old tiles, not slate is in need of repair.

4 The garden – leading down to the sea is a jungle.

Brackets are often used for longer parentheses, especially if they include a verb.

- The castle is really old (Henry built it 500 years ago).

Watch the punctuation at the end of the brackets!

Activity 3

Add parentheses (in brackets) to these sentences.

1 The knights (...) rode their horses there.

_____

2 The drawbridge was wooden (...) and it was usually raised.

_____

3 The moat was full of water (...).

_____

4 I always forget the date (...).

_____

5 I hope to go back there (...).

_____

Activity 4

You can also use pairs of commas for parenthesis.

In some of these sentences they may not both be there; add the missing commas.

1 The newer house built this century, is in the grounds of the old house.

2 The drive leading up to the old house, is moss and gravel.

3 The roof of old broken tiles, is in need of repair.

4 The garden, leading down to the sea is a jungle.

5 The out-houses and out is the word, are right across the yard.

24: Punctuation – Hyphens

The hyphen is a much shorter dash, used to connect words or parts of a word: sixty-five, re-enter, well-known, man-eating.

Activity 1

The first use of hyphens is to make compound words, like parade-ground.

Very common compound words don't have hyphens, like toothbrush and moonlight.

Rewrite those you think need a hyphen to make the meaning clear.

1 carryon _____

2 overegg _____

3 ovenready_____

4 oxeye _____

5 housetrain _____

6 copilot _____

7 calfskin _____

8 campfire _____

9 candlestick_____

10 hollyhock _____

Activity 2

The second use of hyphens is for prefixes, especially where there are two vowels together.

Again, rewrite those you think need a hyphen to make the meaning clear.

1 readvertise _____

2 realign _____

3 reelect _____

4 reedit _____

5 reeducate_____

6 reemerge _____

7 reequip _____

8 reinforce _____

9 reopen_____

10 reoccupy_____

11 rerelease _____

12 reunite _____

The third use of hyphens is to link connected adjectives before a noun: thirteenth-century castle; ten-year-old girl; six-metre fence.

Rewrite these phrases with the adjectives as words before the noun.

1 motorway from the 20th century

_____

2 man aged 65

_____

3 ditch 3 metres deep

_____

4 wall 6 metres tall

_____

The fourth use of hyphens is to avoid confusion or ambiguity.

Rewrite these sentences with hyphens, to make the meaning clear.

1 I found the man eating sharks very scary.

_____

2 The well kept well looks well.

_____

3 The fast growing runner is only ten.

_____

4 The early medieval breakfast was served at 8 o'clock.

_____

25: Punctuation – Bullets and lists

When you make a list, you can number the points; or use letters; or use bullet points.

To punctuate your bullet points:

- If it's a complete sentence, use a capital letter and a full stop.
- Long phrases: capital at the beginning, no full stop
- Short phrases: all lower case

Activity 1

You have won the lottery! Make a bullet-point list of what you'd spend your money on.

Activity 2

This time try using numbered points.

You have just been made Prime Minister! List what you would do to help the country.

It is tricky to punctuate direct speech correctly, but you can look at any novel for a model.

> "Here we are," she said. "Let's start immediately."
>
> "Oh no," he said, "it's not time yet."
>
> "Why not?" she said. "It's surely time," as she wiped her nose.
>
> He replied, "Very well, let's begin."

Activity 1

Write out the speech bubbles as direct speech.

"Put him down," said the foreman.

_____

_____

_____

_____

_____

Activity 2

Now write out this conversation, breaking the direct speech in the middle sometimes.

You could also add a bit of description before and after.

It's about the town of Caernarfon at the end of the 13th century.

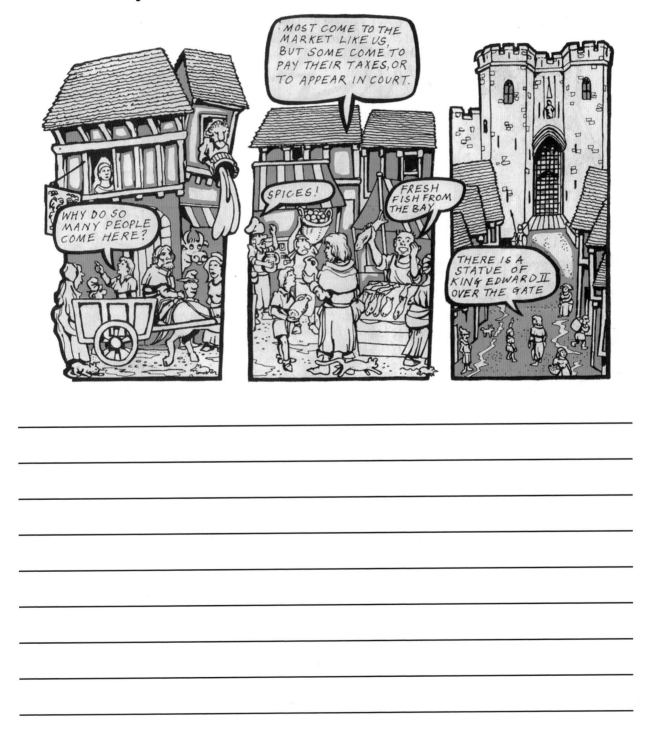

27: Punctuation and Spelling – Apostrophes

The apostrophe may be a **punctuation** mark, but it's also about **spelling** the word it's in, and understanding the **grammar** of the word.

Activity 1

We'll start with the apostrophe for missing letters, called a **contraction**.

Write the contractions for these forms, some are positive, some negative.

1 I had ridden _____

2 I have been _____

3 you are sure _____

4 you have said _____

5 he has not come _____

6 she would not say _____

7 it is raining _____

8 it has been snowing _____

9 we must not say _____

10 we would not decide _____

11 we could not come _____

12 they have said _____

13 they are running _____

The second main use of the apostrophe is for ownership or possession.

But interestingly this also used to be about marking a missing letter: the old spelling was **the kinges crown**, which then got shortened to **the king's crown**.

Remember the rules for where to put the apostrophe:

- if there's one owner, after the owner and before the s
- if there are plural owners, after the owners, so after the s
- if it's an irregular plural that doesn't end in s, after the owners and before the s.

Activity 2

Write in the possessive phrases, following the style.

1 One driver has one car _The driver's car_

2 Two drivers share one car _____

3 Two men share one car _____

4 Two women share one car _____

5 One woman has two cars _____

6 One woman has three sons _____

7 Two ladies own two hats _____

8 Two grannies own several teapots _____

9 The children have several toys _____

10 Milk from goats _____

11 Milk from sheep _____

Answers

1: Spelling – Prefixes

Activity 1: undo: to take apart; incorrect: not right; disappear: to go away; mistake: do something wrong; prefab: made before; replace: to put back again; submarine: below the sea; intercity: between cities; supermarket: large shop; antibiotic: against germs; autograph: signed by yourself

2: Spelling – Suffixes

Activity 1: happiness, happily; airiness, airily; boldness, boldly; tidiness, tidily; easiness, easily; coolness, coolly; cosiness, cosily; daftness, daftly; holiness, holily; fairness, fairly; laziness, lazily; woolliness, woollily; business, busily

Activity 2: playing, player; dancing, dancer; binding, binder; folding, folder; mixing, mixer; caring, carer; skating, skater; mincing, mincer; painting, painter; drawing, drawer; mashing, masher

Activity 3: crying, cried; replying, replied; relying, relied; spying, spied

3: Spelling – Short and long vowels

Activity 2: For example:

	Short vowel sound	Long vowel sound
a	dab, dam	date, day, dale
e	den, deck	deep, dream
i	din, dim	dine, dice
o	dot, dog	dote, dole
u	dug, duck	dune, duke

Activity 3: mat mate, met mete, bit bite, rod rode, dun dune, sham shame, pet Pete, fin fine, hop hope, tun tune

4: Spelling – Suffixes after short vowels

Activity 1: flicking, flicked, flicker; tending, tended, tender; sifting, sifted, sifter; sanding, sanded, sander; bumping, bumped, bumper; longing, longed, longer; clanging, clanged, clanger; hanging, hanged, hanger; knocking, knocked, knocker; wrecking, wrecked, wrecker

Activity 2: mixing, mixed, mixer; fixing, fixed, fixer; boxing, boxed, boxer

Activity 3: trapping, trapped, trapper; stopping, stopped, stopper; matting, matted, matter; betting, betted, better; patting, patted, patter; dipping, dipped, dipper; wetting, wetted, wetter; potting, potted, potter; fitting, fitted, fitter; rotting, rotted, rotter; hamming, hammed, hammer; shopping, shopped, shopper; supping, supped, supper

Activity 4: twining, caned, striped, tiny, robed, bony, taping, moping, mated, piped, fusing, pining, super, diner

5: Spelling – Suffix -ant and -ent

Activity 1: dominant, jubilant, stagnant, expectant, observant, tolerant, ignorant, abundant, resonant

Activity 2: attendant, assistant, claimant, immigrant, litigant, occupant

Activity 3: lenient, obedient, affluent, confident, decadent, impudent, independent, coherent, indulgent, diligent, convergent, divergent, emergent, decent, frequent, eloquent

6: Spelling – Suffix -able and -ible

Activity 1: applicable, considerable, observable, tolerable, understandable, reasonable, comfortable, enjoyable, fixable

Activity 2: biddable, reliable, sizable, likable, movable, changeable, noticeable, serviceable, believable

Activity 3: possible, horrible, legible, incredible, sensible, terrible, visible

Activity 4: -able words: lovable, reliable, unflappable, changeable, winnable
-ible words: credible, horrible, possible, visible, feasible

7: Spelling – Silent letters

Activity 1: thumb, lamb, crumb; gnome, gnaw, gnash; knife, knit, knock; write, wrong, wrist

Activity 3: night, light, tight, right, bright, bought, fought, sought, thought, caught, taught

8: Spelling – Homophones

Activity 1: practise, license, prophesy, device, advice

10: Spelling and Grammar – Word classes

Activity 1: harmonic, harmonise; glorious, glorify; peaceful, pacify; believable, believe; practical, practise; advisable, advise; glamorous, glamorise; successful, succeed; fatty, fatten

11: Spelling and Grammar – Using a dictionary

Activity 1: 1 public and punctual **2** start with 'pub' **3** plural **4** -es, -ing, -ed **5** puff
6 italic

12: Grammar – Spoken/written English

Activity 2: 1 I have never seen him before. **2** It's as if I had never left. **3** You have done well. **4** I'm doing well. **5** You will love your mobile phone with all your heart. **6** The Great Debate. **7** To be or not to be.

14: Grammar – Pronouns

Activity 1: 1 He lost it. **2** She was cross with him. **3** He accused them. **4** They came to see us. **5** She found it before he did. **6** They were both pleased.

Activity 2: 1 My bike goes faster than his. **2** My bike is smaller than hers. **3** Your car is bigger than theirs. **4** Mine is faster than his. **5** Theirs is bigger than ours.

15: Grammar – Verbs

Activity 1: 1 The news was watched by everyone today. **2** We were struck by how horrifying the figures were. **3** We were told by the newsreader what would happen next. **4** It was thought by all of us to be a disaster. **5** Nothing similar was remembered by anybody. **6** It will be remembered by everyone for a long time.

Activity 2: 1 Scientists fully research their experiments. **2** They usually write notes with long sentences. **3** Journals publish their research. **4** Very few people read the journals. **5** People award scientists lots of prizes. **6** Will anyone remember them?

16: Grammar – Adverbs

Activity 1: 1 more quietly, most quietly **2** harder, hardest **3** more swiftly, most swiftly **4** worse, worst **5** farther, farthest **6** earlier, earliest

18: Grammar – Relative clauses

Activity 1: 1 was designed **2** was **3** would land **4** went off **5** shared **6** was loaded

19: Grammar – Conjunctions

Activity 1: 1 Those are my socks, whose holes need darning. **2** I buy my socks at that shop, where there's a cafe upstairs. **3** I bought them last week, when I really needed them. **4** I shall give them to my sister, who likes them too.

Activity 2: For example: **1** I'm on the bus as I'm going swimming. **2** It's cold outside, but it's warm in the pool. **3** I'll meet my friends there, because they all go there too. **4** We like the other pool better, and it's longer.

Activity 3: For example: **1** I get up, then I have my breakfast. **2** I eat lunch, and next I go out to play. **3** I have tea before I meet my friends. **4** After I play games, I go to bed.

Activity 4: For example: **1** Because I'm hungry, I eat my tea. **2** Since I'm thirsty, I get a drink. **3** If I'm tired, I go to sleep. **4** Although I'm tired, I can't sleep.

20: Grammar and Punctuation – Phrases

Activity 1: 1 Coming in softly, he made no noise at all. **2** For the last time, don't forget the butter! **3** I always think, staying in the country, that it's the best place to be. **4** My home, round the corner from the canal, is easy to find. **5** I always daydream, on the way home. **6** That's where you'll find me, just north of the canal.

Activity 2: 1 I'm always hungry coming home from school. **2** I really enjoy my tea after a hard day's football practice. **3** I'm going out this evening, always a nice thing to do. **4** I'll be back early, probably very tired. **5** Then it's school tomorrow, my favourite lessons of the week.

Activity 3: 1 Getting up late and missing breakfast is never a good idea. **2** The man with the hairy beard and messy hair was waiting at the bus stop. **3** The girl with the dragon tattoo is a scary person. **4** The girl, her sister and her dolls are all packed and ready. **5** Despite the rain, wearing wellington boots still looks silly.

21: Grammar and Punctuation – Clauses

Activity 3: 1 I'll add commas to those that need them. **2** The second sentence, which definitely needs a comma, is easier to do. **3** This is the second sentence that might need a comma. **4** This is a good exercise, where commas are concerned. **5** The exercises that use commas are the best ones. **6** Those sentences that use commas are easier to do. **7** The last sentence, which is missing a comma, doesn't make sense. **8** This is the last sentence that I'm going to do.

22: Punctuation – Semicolons and colons

Activity 2: 2 At lunch I drink cold water; at supper I drink juice. **3** In the summer it rains a lot; in the winter it rains less. **4** At bedtime I clean my teeth for two minutes; in the morning I clean them rather longer.

23: Punctuation – Dashes and brackets

Activity 1: 1 I expect he'll be late: he usually is. **2** What's the world coming to? I wish I knew. **3** He said it was for charity; that's his story, anyway. **4** I know I said it; and I meant it.

Activity 2: 1 The newer house – built this century – is in the grounds of the old house. **2** The drive – leading up to the old house – is moss and gravel. **3** The roof – old tiles, not slate – is in need of repair. **4** The garden – leading down to the sea – is a jungle.

Activity 4: 1 The newer house, built this century, is in the grounds of the old house. **2** The drive, leading up to the old house, is moss and gravel. **3** The roof, of old broken tiles, is in need of repair. **4** The garden, leading down to the sea, is a jungle. **5** The out-houses, and out is the word, are right across the yard.

24: Punctuation – Hyphens

Activity 1: carry-on, over-egg, oven-ready, ox-eye, house-train, co-pilot

Activity 2: re-advertise, realign, re-elect, re-edit, re-educate, re-emerge, re-equip, reinforce, reopen, reoccupy, re-release, reunite

Activity 3: 1 twentieth-century motorway **2** sixty-five-year-old man **3** three-metre-deep ditch **4** six-metre-tall wall

Activity 4: 1 I found the man-eating sharks very scary. **2** The well-kept well looks well. **3** The fast-growing runner is only ten. **4** The early-medieval breakfast was served at 8 o'clock.

26: Punctuation – Direct speech

Activity 1: "Put him down," said the foreman.
"Richard of Radwell, Mason," said the first man.
"There are no hills like these in Norfolk," said another man.
"Nor in Holland," replied his mate.
"For the mill," said a man with a huge millstone.

Activity 2: "Why do so many people come here?" asked the man in a cart.
"Most come to the market like us," replied one shopper, "but some come to pay their taxes, or to appear in court."
"Spices!" called one trader.
"Fresh fish from the bay!" called another.
"There is a statue of King Edward II over the gate," remarked someone in the street.

27: Punctuation and Spelling – Apostrophes

Activity 1: 1 I'd ridden **2** I've been **3** you're sure **4** you've said **5** he hasn't come **6** she wouldn't say **7** it's raining **8** it's been snowing **9** we mustn't say **10** we wouldn't decide **11** we couldn't come **12** they've said **13** they're running

Activity 2: 2 The drivers' car **3** The men's car **4** The women's car **5** The woman's cars **6** The woman's sons **7** The ladies' hats **8** The grannies' teapots **9** The children's toys **10** Goats' milk **11** Sheep's milk

The UK's biggest home-learning range

WHSmith

These **WHSmith English Practice Workbooks** are available for **ages 7–11**

Maths titles are also available.

Your Learning Journey

The comprehensive range of **WHSmith** home-learning books forms a Learning Journey that supports children's education and helps to prepare for every success at school. We support children – and parents – through every step of that journey.

Practice — Reinforces classroom core skills

Challenge — Stretches more-able children

Progress — 10-minute progress checks

Revision — Develop skills for tests

Test — Practice for National Tests

Practice

The **WHSmith Practice Workbooks** for key stage 2 provide extra activities and support, building your child's confidence and understanding.

+ Plenty of practice to boost confidence
+ Write well and be understood
+ More fun activities for you to work through at home
+ Written by experienced teachers

For more information plus advice and support for parents visit
www.whsmith.co.uk/readytoprogress

Shop online at whsmith.co.uk
WH Smith Retail Ltd SN3 3RX

ISBN 978-1-4441-8870-7
9 781444 188707